Mopatop's Shop™

You want it?
We've got it!
Mopatop has got it.
Everything to make
your dreams come true.
You need it?
They stock it.
Puppyduck,
she's got it.
You won't
believe the things
we've got on view.
Delicious surprises,
before your very eyes.
A scratch, a smile,
a shake, a shine,
a shoe!
When you go out shoppin',
why don't you just pop in.
Mopatop's the shop
for me and you!

Annual 2000

This Mopatop's Shop Annual belongs to:

_____

_____

_____

DK

www.dk.com

Author   Vicci Parr
Designers   Mandy Sherliker and Ness Wood
Managing Editor   Joanna Devereux
Managing Art Editor   Chris Fraser
Production   Linda Dare
DTP Designer   Jill Bunyan
Upsy Daisy/Original TV Script   Sally-Ann Lever
Upsy Daisy/Story Adaptation   Caryn Jenner
Photography   Dave King
Illustrations   Anne Matthews/Denis Ryan

First published in Great Britain in 1999 by
Dorling Kindersley Limited,
9 Henrietta Street, London WC2E 8PS

A CIP record for this book is available from the
British Library.

ISBN 0-7513-6680-3

Colour reproduction by
Dot Gradations Limited
Printed and bound in Italy by
L.E.G.O.

Mopatop's Shop™ Annual

Contents

Welcome to Mopatop's Shop

Oh hello! Welcome to
Mopatop's Shop.
I'm Mopatop
and this is my shop...

And I'm
Puppyduck!

Tell the Time

The Big Clock tells Mopatop when it is time to open the shop. Look at the little clocks and tell Mopatop what time he has to wake up, eat his lunch and go to bed.

Time to wake up

Lunch time

Bedtime

Copy and Colour

In Mopatop's shop there are lots of pictures in the Picture Department. There is a picture of...

Mopatop

Puppyduck

Mopatop

Puppyduck

Copy the pictures of Mopatop, Puppyduck and Moosey into the blank picture frames and colour them in.

Draw a picture of yourself in the frame below and write your name in the space!

Moosey

Moosey

Hide and Seek!

Where are Mopatop and all his friends? Look at the pictures below and see if you can find Mopatop and all his friends in the big picture opposite. When you find each of them draw a tick in the correct box.

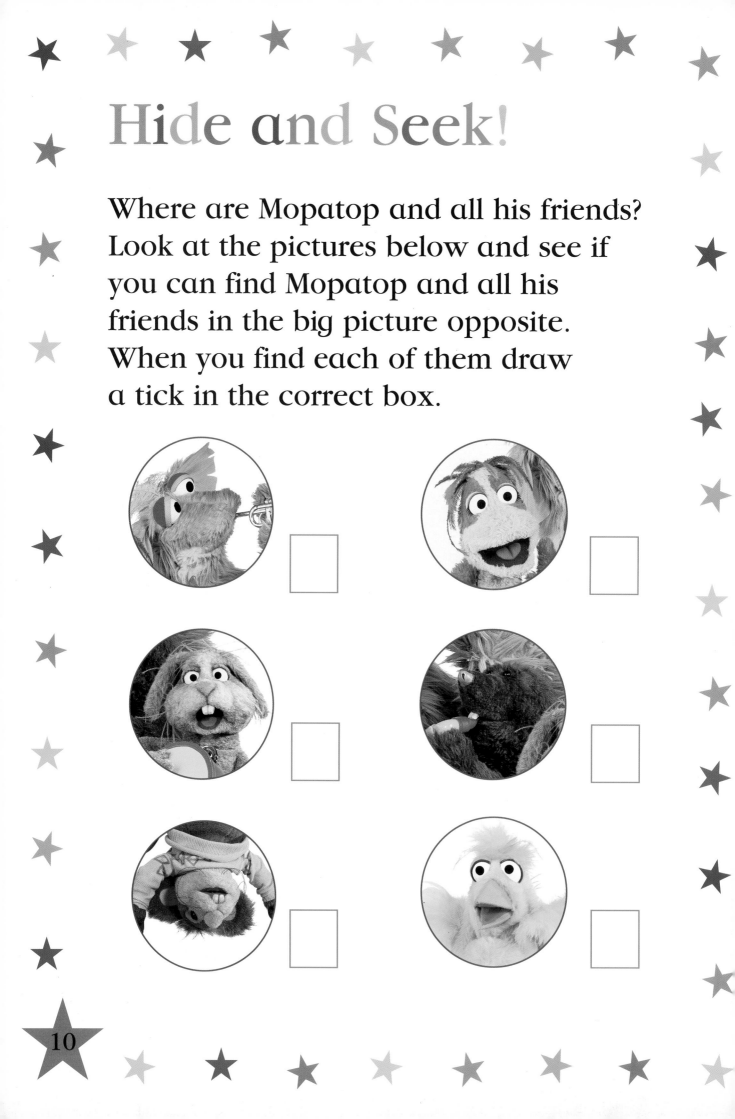

Jam Sandwiches

Puppyduck's favourite thing in the whole world is a jam sandwich. Do you know how to make a jam sandwich? Get an adult to help you follow the pictures. Be careful you don't get sticky fingers!

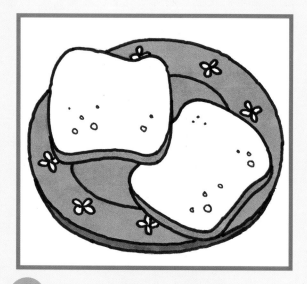

1. First you will need some bread.

2. Next, you will need butter…

3. ...and lots of strawberry jam!

4. Spread the butter and jam onto the bread.

5. Enjoy your sandwiches and don't forget to share them!

13

Animal Magic

In the Mixed-up Animal Department there are lots of mixed-up animals. Puppyduck also looks like a mixed-up animal – a puppy and a duck! Mix two of your favourite animals together and draw your new animal below.

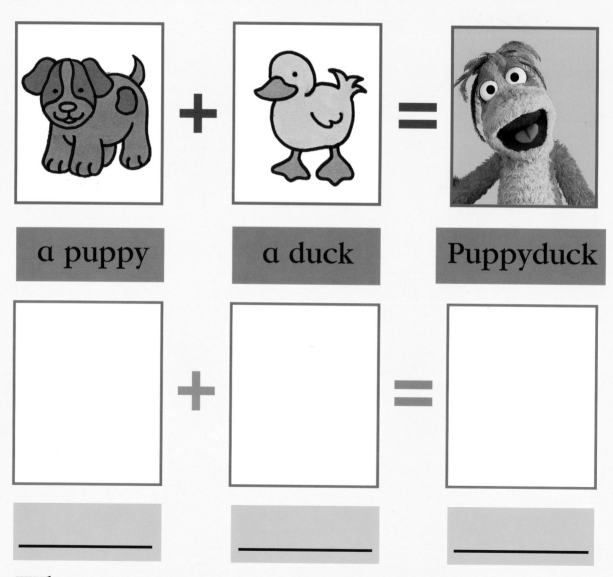

a puppy + a duck = Puppyduck

+ =

____ ____ ____

What is your new animal called?

Jigsaw Jumble

Trace the jigsaw pieces onto some paper. Get an adult to help you cut out the pieces and then stick them onto some card. Colour the pieces in and your jigsaw is ready to do!

Upsy Daisy

Original TV script by Sally-Ann Lever
Story adaptation by Caryn Jenner

It was time for Mopatop to open his shop.
"Welcome to Mopatop's Shop," he said.
"Would you like a cosy little bed? Or lots of
pretty red? Or a bunny on his head?"

DING!
The shop bell rang and
in walked a possum
with a toolbox.
"I'm Upsy Daisy," said
the possum.
"Of course! I forgot you
were coming today,"
said Mopatop.
"I'll get to work right
away," said Upsy Daisy.

19

"Hello, Mopatop!" Puppyduck called. "What's going on?" "Upsy Daisy is fixing up something special for us."

"What is it?" asked Puppyduck.

"It's a surprise," said Mopatop with a smile.

"All done," said Upsy Daisy. "Payment will be one poem, please."

Mopatop cleared his throat:

Thank you, thank you, Upsy Daisy,
It's plain to see you are not lazy.
I soon will try the button out,
It's sure to work, I have no doubt.

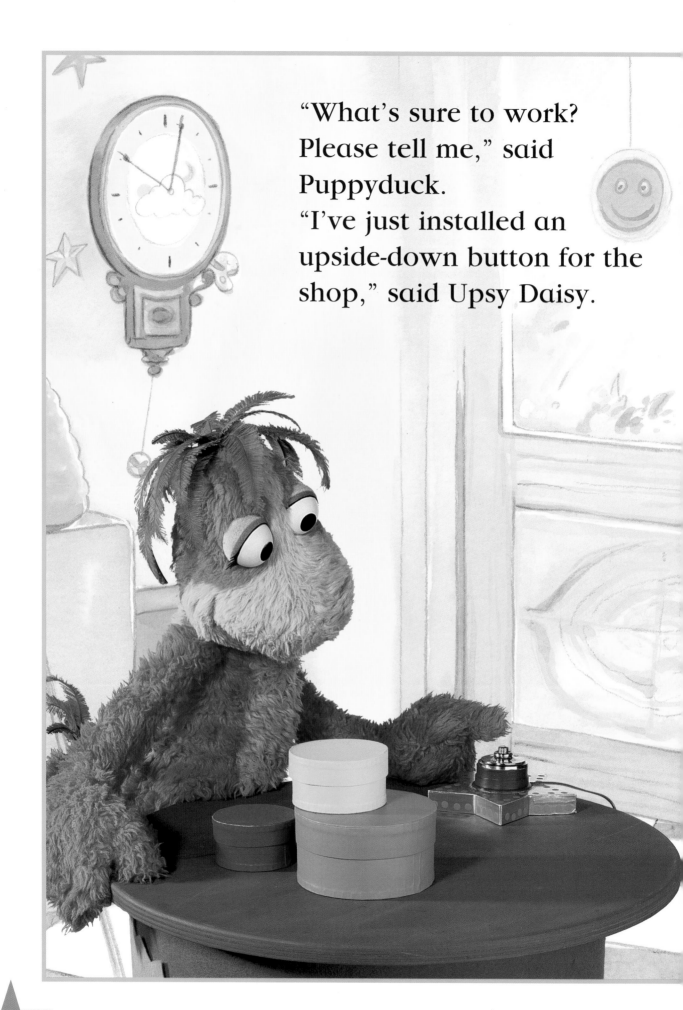

"What's sure to work? Please tell me," said Puppyduck.
"I've just installed an upside-down button for the shop," said Upsy Daisy.

"You mean that if I press this button, I'll be upside down?" asked Puppyduck. "You certainly will," said Mopatop.

"The whole shop will be upside down," said Upsy Daisy. "Call me if you have any problems. Bye!" Puppyduck pressed the button.

Suddenly, the shop turned upside down.
Puppyduck didn't like being upside down.
"I feel weird," she said. "The floor is now
the ceiling."

"Mopatop, please turn the shop right-side up again," cried Puppyduck.
"All right," said Mopatop, and he pressed the button.

The shop turned right-side up.
DING!
"Here comes a customer," said Mopatop.
The customer was a big furry animal.
"Hello, I'm a gnu. I saw your shop turn
upside down and I was wondering if I could
try some upside down, too!"
Mopatop pressed the button.

The shop turned upside down again.
Moosey was in the attic. "Oh no, not again!"
he groaned.
"What's wrong, dear?" asked Mother Mouse.
"Don't you like being upside down?"

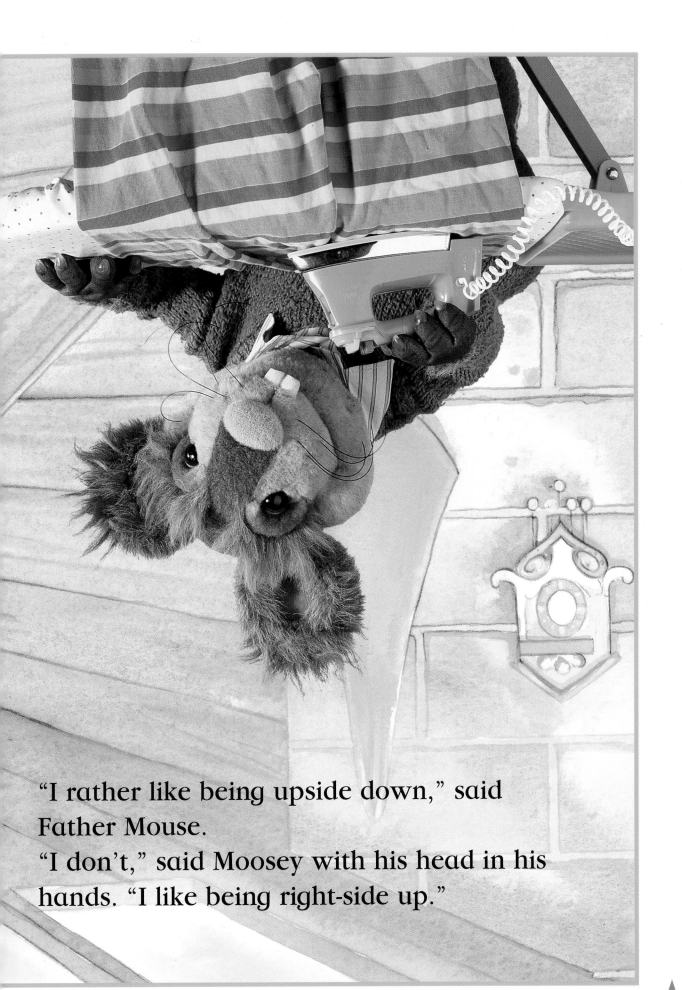

"I rather like being upside down," said
Father Mouse.
"I don't," said Moosey with his head in his
hands. "I like being right-side up."

"This is excellent," said
the gnu. "How do we
get right-side up again?"
"Like this," said Mopatop,
pressing the button.
Nothing happened.
Mopatop frowned. "The button
is stuck. We'll have to call
Upsy Daisy."
All together they called, "UPSY DAISY!"

DING!

As soon as Upsy Daisy walked through the door of the shop, she turned upside down. "You called?" she said.

"Yes," said Mopatop. "The button is stuck."

"Can you fix it, please?" asked Puppyduck.

"Of course I can fix it," said Upsy Daisy.
"But I'll need an upside-down song first."
"I can't sing upside down!" said Puppyduck.

Mopatop and the
gnu sang:
The world's turned upside down,
The bottom's now the top.

I much prefer the way it was,
The time has come to STOP!
finished Puppyduck.

"That was a beautiful song. Thank you," said Upsy Daisy. "Now I will fix your upside-down button."
Upsy Daisy got out her tools and went straight to work.

Suddenly, the shop turned right-side up. "Hooray!" cheered Puppyduck.

But a moment later, everything was upside down again. The attic was upside down, too. "Oh no," groaned Moosey. "I want to be right-side up."

Suddenly, he *was* right-side up.
"At last, somebody's listening to me," said
Moosey. "I don't feel very well at all."
"This is rather fun," said Father Mouse.

In the shop, the gnu turned to leave.
"Thank you very much for showing me
upside down."
"My pleasure," said Mopatop. "Goodbye!"
Upsy Daisy put her tools away.
"I've got some bad news, Mopatop.
Your upside-down button
is broken."

"I don't think we need an upside-down button after all," Mopatop told Upsy Daisy.

"But what about the poem and the song you gave me?" she asked.

"Will you be wanting
them back now?"
"Poems and songs are
for sharing," said
Mopatop.
"Oh, thank you!"
And Upsy Daisy sang all
the way out of the shop.

43

Just then, the big clock chimed.
"That means it's time to close the shop," said
Mopatop. "Puppyduck, where are you?"

Mopatop looked all over
the shop.
"I'm over here!" said a
voice from behind the
little door.

Mopatop opened
the little door.
"Bunny and I
were practising
upside down," said
Puppyduck.
Mopatop laughed.

Moosey's Question Time

Now you've read the story see if you can answer the following questions.

1. What colour rhymes with the words, bed and head?

2. What kind of animal is Upsy Daisy?

3. What did Mopatop order from Upsy Daisy for the shop?

4. What kind of animal wanted to try some upside down with Mopatop and Puppyduck?

5. Did Moosey like being upside down?

6. How does Mopatop know when it is time to close the shop?

Spot the Difference

Look at the top picture, then find five differences in the bottom picture. Draw a circle round the differences when you find them.

Colouring In

Mopatop has found a picture of himself, Puppyduck and Moosey. Can you colour it in for him so that he can put it in the Colourful Pictures Department?

Moosey's Maze

Lamont delivers a special box to Mopatop's shop. It is a box full of surprises and Moosey wants to look inside. Help him to find his way from the attic to the box.

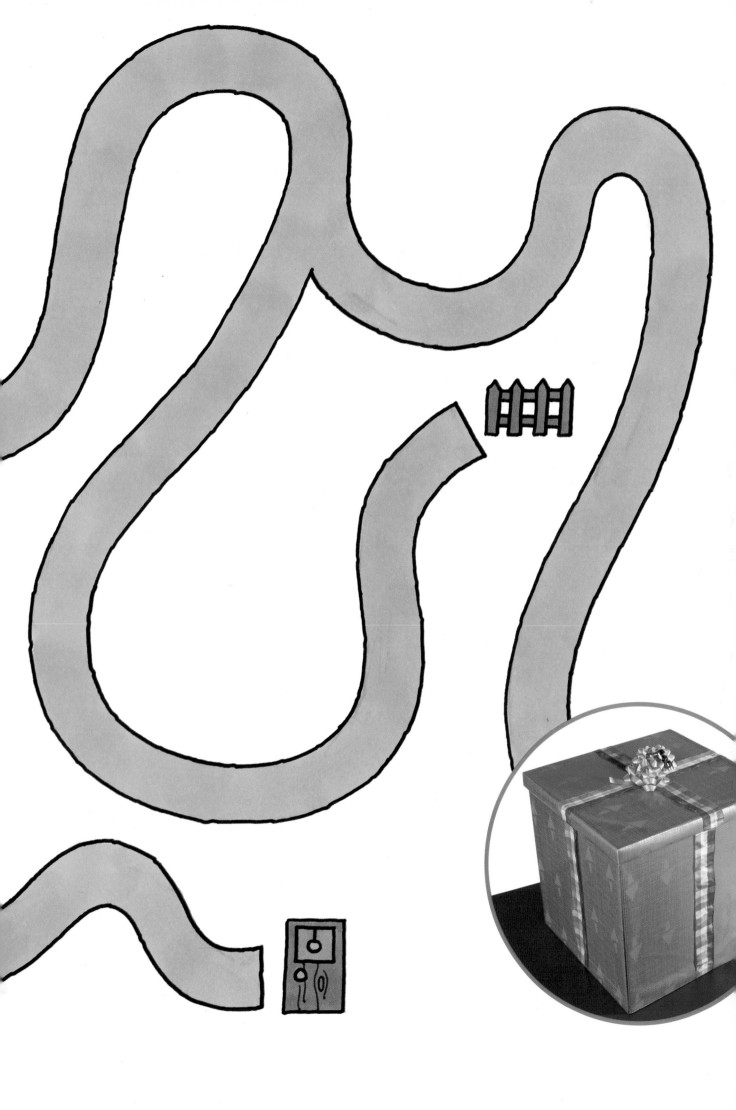

Sounds like a ...

The cheeses are making animal noises and Mopatop thinks there are animals in the shop! Follow the lines from the cheeses to find out which animals they are trying to be.

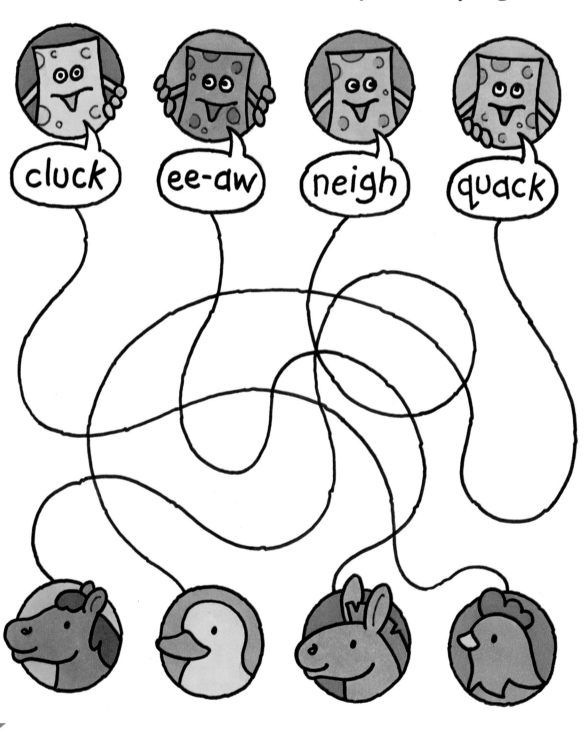

Gerald's Word Square

Odd-job Gerald had fixed five things in Mopatop's shop today. Look at their pictures below and then find them in the word square. All the words are written across.

c	h	a	i	r	b	f	g	x	t
s	u	d	k	a	p	t	q	j	c
y	k	t	a	b	l	e	v	a	f
r	c	m	y	e	d	b	h	l	g
a	u	g	b	o	s	n	w	i	o
v	t	e	l	e	p	h	o	n	e
z	i	o	j	z	s	u	k	a	t
c	l	o	c	k	r	d	s	q	f
t	x	q	s	m	x	p	f	m	w
l	h	n	v	r	u	d	o	o	r

telephone   table   door   clock   chair

What's the Weather?

Mopatop and Puppyduck have put their umbrellas up because it is raining. Puppyduck likes the rain but Mopatop likes the sun! Which is your favourite?

Look at the pictures below and help
Mopatop and Puppyduck to put the
correct labels under each picture.
Copy the labels in the blank spaces.

lightning   fog   snow   wind   rain   sun

Splish! Splash!

In the attic, Moosey is taking a  .

There are lots of  all over the

floor. Downstairs,  hears

a .  and look all

over the . Suddenly, the

opens and  enters the .

 wants a  . He

wants to wear his new  and

56

splash in a 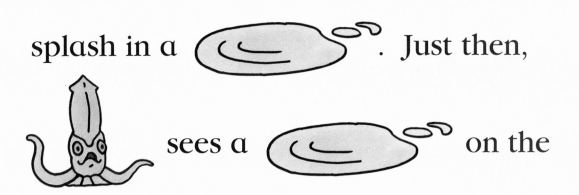. Just then, sees a on the

floor. He begins to splash and sing.

and sing along too!

Party Time!

Bonnie the Bunny invites Mopatop and Puppyduck to her birthday party. Puppyduck loves parties, and Mopatop has made a big cake with lots of candles especially for Bonnie.

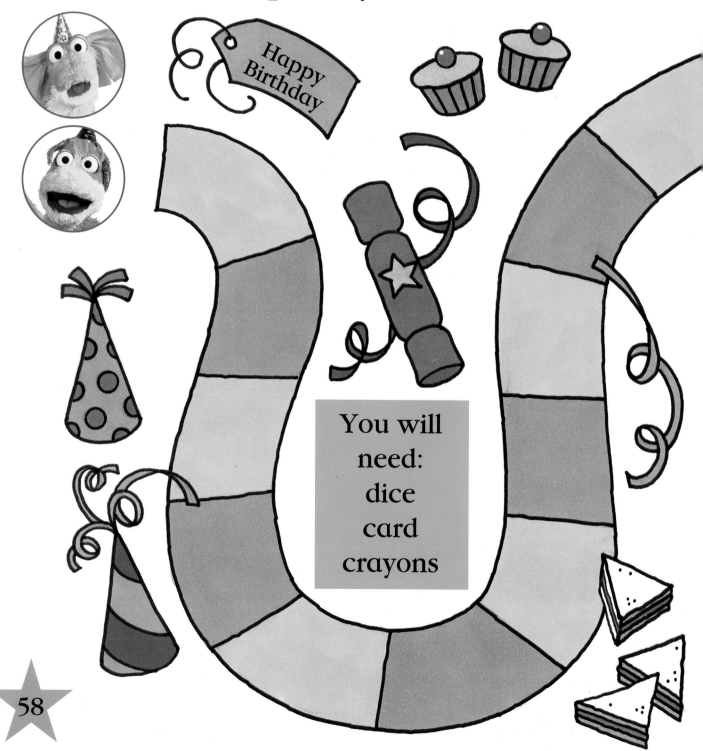

Happy Birthday

You will need:
dice
card
crayons

Make two counters using the card and crayons. Decide who will begin first and then take it in turns to throw the dice, working your way along the squares until you get to the party. Good luck!

Happy Birthday

Goodbye

And there goes the Big Clock. Time to close the shop. I hope we see you again soon. Very, very soon! Goodbye!

Answers

Tell the Time
(page 7)
1. Time to wake up – 8 o'clock
2. Lunch time – 1 o'clock
3. Bedtime – 6 o'clock

Moosey's Question Time
(page 47)
1. Red
2. A possum
3. An upside-down button
4. The gnu
5. No
6. The Big Clock chimes

Spot the Difference
(page 48)
1. Gnu
2. Mother Mouse
3. Flower on sign
4. Bird in a tree with Moosey
5. Flower on Upsy Daisy's hat

Moosey's Maze
(page 50)

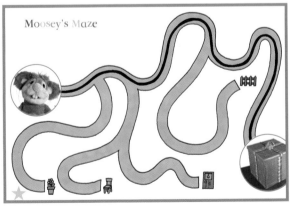

Sounds like a...
(page 52)
A chicken goes cluck
A donkey goes ee-aw
A horse goes neigh
A duck goes quack

Gerald's Word Square
(page 53)

You want it?
We've got it!
Mopatop has got it.
You won't believe
the things we've
got on show.
You need it?
We stock it!
Puppyduck has got it.
But now it seems it's
time for us to go!
The time has
come to stop,
and it's time to
close the shop.
But we will be back
before you know!